TECHNOLOGY AND LIFE ISSUES

POPE JOHN PAUL II
LECTURE SERIES IN BIOETHICS
edited by

Rev. Francis J. Lescoe, Ph.D.

and

Rev. David Q. Liptak, D. Min.

· ·

VOL. III
TECHNOLOGY AND LIFE ISSUES

I. TECHNOLOGIZED PARENTHOOD
by
Donald DeMarco
Professor of Philosophy
University of St. Jerome's College, Ontario

II. THE ETHICS OF SUICIDE
by
Ralph McInerny
Director, Jacques Maritain Center
University of Notre Dame

III. HUMANAE VITAE and FAMILIARIS CONSORTIO IN THE SEMINARY CURRICULUM
by
David Q. Liptak
Professor of Theology
Holy Apostles College and Seminary

POPE JOHN PAUL II BIOETHICS CENTER

ISBN 1-879597-00-4

Lescoe, Francis J. and Liptak, David Q., Editors
Pope John Paul II Lecture Series in Bioethics, Vol. III
DeMarco, Donald, McInerny, Ralph and Liptak, David
TECHNOLOGY AND LIFE ISSUES

IMPRIMATUR
+Daniel P. Reilly, D.D.
Bishop of Norwich
March 27, 1991

NIHIL OBSTAT
Valdemar M. Cukuras, Ph.D., S.T.D.
Censor Deputatus

Distributed by:
  Holy Apostles Seminary Press
  33 Prospect Hill Road
  Cromwell, CT 06416

ANNOUNCEMENT

The Pope John Paul II Bioethics Center has been instituted for the purpose of articulating authentic Catholic teaching with respect to medical science and technology.

In his first encyclical, Redemptor Hominis, *John Paul defended the priority of ethics over science and technology:*

> *The development of technology and the development of contemporary civilization, which is marked by the ascendancy of technology, demand a proportional development of morals and ethics. (Section 16)*

Today, with an unprecedented rush of scientific discoveries and technological breakthroughs, this priority is being doubted, ignored and challenged. Traditional Christian principles repeatedly affirmed by the Church's magisterium, have been set aside for consequentialism, behaviorism, relativism, context morality, secularism and other inadequate or erroneous theories in misleading, false and sometimes inane attempts to address ethically fresh scientific insights or revolutionary technological advances.

The purpose of this Center is twofold. First, we shall endeavor to impart to our seminarians, here at Holy Apostles College and Seminary, a solid foundation in medical ethics and bioethical science. Secondly, we shall share our investigations and findings by publishing periodic monographs, in addition to the annual Pope John Paul II Lectures in Bioethics.

THE POPE JOHN PAUL II LECTURES
IN BIOETHICS
HAVE BEEN MADE POSSIBLE THROUGH
THE GENEROSITY OF
REVEREND LEO J. KINSELLA
OUR LADY OF THE SNOWS
CHICAGO, ILLINOIS

TABLE OF CONTENTS

I. TECHNOLOGIZED PARENTHOOD
By Donald DeMarco

"Technologized parenthood" is a disquieting expression. It represents the introduction of an essentially impersonal factor in an area that is replete with personal and transcendent meaning. Parenthood, which unites the natural with the supernatural, the present with the past and future, and spouses with each other and their progeny, is inevitably imperiled when it is allied with the one-dimensional processes of technologization. Technologized parenthood, then, is an attempt to fuse fundamentally discordant elements. And its inherent danger is in producing a split between technology and moral values, one that would result in the domination by technology of those moral values parenthood needs in order to realize its fulfillment in the distinctive forms of motherhood and fatherhood.

In his book *Mechanization Take Command,* cultural historian Siegfried Giedion details how modern processes of mechanization have brought about a comparable split between thought and feeling. He found this split to be particularly evident in biology, where it is commonplace to exclude feelings (especially those that carry moral implications) in order to bring everything under the reign of thought (for the purpose of rational control). By reducing the living organism to a mere assemblage of material parts, the entire dimension of feeling is thereby made irrelevant. According to Giedion, "in *biology* the animate being was considered simply as the sum of its separate parts assembled like those of a machine. Organic processes were regarded as purely physico-chemical in nature, as if an organism were a kind of chemical plant." [1]

Marshall McLuhan titled his first book *The Mechanical Bride* (1951) in order to jolt his readers into realizing that to the blind processes of mechanization and technologization nothing is sacred. Not even a bride, the quintessential image of unravished loveliness, would be spared. As a sequel to this work, McLuhan wrote *Culture is Our Business* (1970) to show how technology has crested modern culture itself.

McLuhan's claims are amply validated by the contemporary verbal hybrid that are the logical offspring of our age of the "Mechanical Bride." Thus, we speak blandly of artificial flowers, astro-turf, synthetic food, and the bionic man. We watch movies such as *The Love Machine, Heartbeeps, Electric Dreams,* and *The Computer Wore Tennis Shoes.* And we casually incorporate into our daily life such glaring incongruities as artificial intelligence, electronic voice-prints, atomic cocktails, and computer dating. We have been conditioned to take verbal incongruities in stride, thereby preparing the way for the broad cultural acceptance of genetic engineering, test-tube babies, and technologized parenthood.

Surveying the threat that technology poses for life, McLuhan saw an antagonism between "technological determinism" and "organic autonomy," [2] between the total dominance over life by technology and the freedom human organisms need in order to live and reproduce according to personal moral norms.

The invasion of technology into the domain of human sexuality began with contraception, which separates sex from procreation. Technologized parenthood is merely the converse of this separation. Whereas contraception means sex without babies, technologized parenthood means babies without sex (or at least without the fullness of the conjugal union).

Contraceptive sex violates the organic unity of sex and procreation. As a result, it leaves both these factors isolated and unprotected. Organically united, sex and procreation function together as protective complementaries. Procreation protects sex from degenerating into an act that makes pleasure primary; while bodified sex gives procreation a basis in personal intimacy, protecting it from exploitation by laboratory technicians and marketing managers.

The large-scale cultural approbation of contraception has made technologized parenthood unavoidable, even though most people did not realize that when they accepted the separation of sex from procreation they were inaugurating the separation of procreation from sex.

When organic, incarnate unities are separated into isolated parts, a host of separations on moral, spiritual and psychological levels take place concomitantly. One separation in particular is the focus of this discussion. It is the separation, through various modes of technological interventions in human reproduction, of parenthood from either motherhood or fatherhood. The fullness of both mother- and fatherhood demands the unification of procreation and bodified, conjugal love. As this unity is compromised or violated, the moral and spiritual meanings of mother- and fatherhood are proportionally jeopardized.

At the same time, the separation between parenthood and bodified motherhood and fatherhood is occasioned by the split between thought and feeling. In this context, such a split is tantamount to separating the desire to control reproduction technologically from the willingness to recognize and protect the qualities that are peculiar to mother- and fatherhood. Parenthood in its most elementary form is achieved whenever there is the slenderest biological connection between progenitor and offspring. Parenthood is something humans share with all species of the animal and plant kingdoms. But mother- and fatherhood possess moral and spiritual dimensions that mere parenthood lacks. It is precisely these dimensions that are at risk whenever there is an attempt to technologize parenthood.

We will examine five specific modes of technologized reproduction in order to illustrate the fundamental antagonism that exists between technologized parenthood and incarnate mother- and fatherhood. These modes are: 1) artificial insemination; 2) *in vitro* fertilization; 3) embryo transfer; 4) extracorporeal gestation; 5) surrogate motherhood.

1) Artificial Insemination

In 1884, a wealthy Philadelphia couple approached Dr. William Pancoast, a medical school professor. The couple had been trying to have a child, but without success. The doctor offered to help. Since the cause of the problem seemed to be with the husband, Pancoast looked for someone to donate semen to be injected into the wife's womb. He invited the best looking student in his class to be the artificial insemination donor (A I D). The student complied and the doctor injected the semen into the woman, which resulted in pregnancy.

Pancoast performed the artificial insemination while the woman was under anesthesia, and had not told her or her husband exactly what he had done. But he saw fit to change his mind once the baby was bore. The infant bore such a striking resemblance to its biological father that Pancoast felt obliged to explain to the husband what really transpired. The rich Philadelphian, happy to have a child, born no grudge against the doctor. He asked only that his wife not be told how the child was conceived. [3]

We may ignore, in this instance, the factors of adultery, rape (involuntary intercourse), and gross deception. Our concerns here have to do with the effect of this technological procedure on the notion of fatherhood. While the Philadelphian was ignorant of the true paternity of the child, he believed that he was the father. After he was told that he was not the father, his wife continued to believe that he was. Thus fatherhood is made so tenuous as to be classified information that may or may not be revealed. At best, it is a mere belief. The husband believes he is not a father, the wife believes he is.

Dr. Pancoast's pioneer experiment in artificial insemination has prepared the way for no end of deception and confusion with regard to fatherhood. Technologized parenthood which allows a third party into the marriage relationship has proven extremely troublesome, even from the legal point of view. In Germany, for example, even a husband who consents to AID can disclaim his paternity anytime during the first two years of the child's life. In the United States, 15 states have laws which make a man who consents to the artificial insemination of his wife the legal father of the child. But in other states where no legal precedents exist, a husband who consents to AID and later changes his mind could conceivably charge his wife with adultery and refuse to support the AID child after a divorce. [4]

In order to avoid certain legal problems involving paternity, some doctors deliberately try to make the identity of the biological father impossible to determine. Dr. A.H. Ansari, an Atlanta, Georgia gynecologist, purposely inseminates a woman with a number of different sperm samples. He writes:

> Even in the same cycle, I may use four different
> donors for that individual. I do this so that if the

case comes to court and they ask who the father
is, it might give the lawyer a hard time to determine
which of the four donors should be sued. As for
the patient, she is just receiving biological material.
She never meets the guy; she doesn't care whose
semen you use. [5]

Not only does technologized parenthood through artificial
insemination make fatherhood tenuous, it creates situations
in which its specific determination is undesirable. Most
medical students who provide semen for the customary fee
of $50 probably do not desire to know whether or not their
"biological material" has made them fathers. For them, such
fatherhood places no moral or legal obligations whatsoever
on them and is purely hypothetical. A sperm donor at the
Tyler Medical Clinic in Los Angeles can contribute two or three
times a week for $20 per "donation." Whether such a donor
has sired tens or even hundreds of offspring is, as far as he
is concerned, a mere abstraction.

A few legal cases in the United States show the extent to
which the AID technology can erode the notion of fatherhood.

In a New York State case, *Adoption of Anonymous*, [6] a woman's
second husband petitions to adopt the child of his wife's first
marriage. Her first husband refuses to consent to the adoption procedures, claiming that he is the father. Confronted by
this legal impediment, the petitioner argues that his consent
is not needed since he is not the father, the child having been
conceived by an anonymous donor. In this case, the judge
ruled the wife's first husband (though not the biological father)
is the "parent" of the child and that his consent is required
for the adoption of the child to another.

It is instructive, however, to note that not all courts have
ruled or reasoned in the same way in similar cases. In California (*People v. Sorensen*, 1968), the Supreme Court reasoned that
"a child conceived through AID does not have a 'natural'
father; that the anonymous donor is not the 'natural' father."[7]
Another New York case (*Gursky v. Gursky*, 1963) went further
in its depreciation of biological fatherhood:

An AID child is not "begotten" by a father who
is not the husband; the donor is anonymous; the
wife does not have sexual intercourse or commit

> adultery with him; if there is any "begetting" it is
> by the doctor who in this specialty is often a
> woman.[8]

A child conceived through artificial insemination may have no natural father, may not be begotten by a father, or may be begotten by a "father" who is a woman! When fatherhood is reduced to the plane of the biological, it edges perilously close to oblivion. At the same time, the other dimensions of fatherhood — psychological, moral, spiritual, and legal — are subjects for the Court's sometimes arbitrary ruling.

Technologized fatherhood unravels the integrated totality of incarnate or unified fatherhood. The result is a separation of fatherhood from parenthood as well as a separation of the spiritual from the material, which greatly weakens father-hood, making it appear nebulous, arbitrary, and even hypo-thetical.

2) In Vitro Fertilization

In artificial insemination, only the male gamete is isolated from the body. In IVF, both the male and female gametes are isolated from the body. Because these gametes can effect conception in a dish, totally apart from the bodified husband and wife, the impression is created that in a technical sense the gametes themselves are the parents.

This impression is not without biological analogues. Parent-hood is conferred upon reproducing protozoans despite the fact that they are single-celled. Moreover, in ordinary mitosis, where somatic cells reproduce through replication, the resulting cells are called "daughter cells." Thus, parenthood is attributed to biological entities of a single cell; why not gametes as well?

The form of technologized parenthood we find with IVF creates the bizarre impression that a married couple's own gametes are challenging their claim to parenthood. This, of course, is reductionism in its extreme form. In a holistic perspective, it is the couple who become parents, not their gametes.

There is a time-honored axiom — *actiones sunt suppositorum* — which means that actions belong to the person. We do not say that my eye sees or that my ear hears or that my feet walk. Rather, we say that I see with my eyes, I hear with my ears, and I walk with my feet. Since the source of our actions is our subjectivity as persons, we attribute our actions to ourselves and not to one or another isolated parts of ourselves. It is I who love, not my heart; it is I who think, not my brain.

Likewise, it is the person who becomes a parent — in a specific way as a mother or father — and not the gametes. Technologized parenthood, drives a wedge between specific parenthood which is predicated of the person, and technologized or material parenthood, which is predicated of the gametes or parts of the person.

By separating the gametes from husband and wife, and effecting new life in a Petri dish, *in vitro* fertilization fractures and fractionalizes incarnate parenthood, thereby allowing parenthood to be equivocally assigned to a variety of impersonal factors and to persons on a limited basis. The very expression "test-tube baby," although just a journalistic creation, nonetheless suggests that the parent is a test-tube. And since the newly formed embryo can be implanted in a woman other than the one who contributed the egg, the gestational woman as well as the genetic woman are both called parents, though neither is a parent in the whole sense. Thus, *in vitro* fertilization creates the possibility of assigning parenthood to a variety of people in diverse ways and for different reasons.

On May 2, 1984, test-tube quadruplets were born in London to a Mrs. Janice Smale, who, according to her account, was married to Mr. Denis Smale. Upon investigation, however, it was learned that despite the name by which she identified herself, Mr. Smale is not her husband, but her boyfriend. "Mrs. Smale" is twice married and living apart from her second husband, pending divorce. Nonetheless, the doctors at Hammersmith Hospital in London fertilized six of her ova with Mr. Smale's sperm and implanted them in her uterus. Of the six embryos implanted, four survived.[9]

All the parties involved in the Smale case accept the moral premise that one need not be a husband before he becomes a father. They also endorse the premise that a wife may bear as many as six children at one time who are fathered by a man other than her own husband. The senior consultant of the hospital, who had been accused of actions "bordering on the unethical," defended his position by stating that it was certainly more ethical than that displayed at Bourn Hall, where embryos were used merely as subjects for research.

By condoning such a procedure, the hospital is significantly weakening parenthood. Approving the separation of fatherhood from husbandhood (Mr. Smale) and husbandhood from fatherhood ("Mrs. Smale's" second husband) is not in the interest of integrated parenthood. Moreover, it lends support to the separation of parenthood from marriage, and procreation from lovemaking. Such a sequence of disconnections cannot but have a harmful effect on full motherhood and fatherhood.

Technologized parenthood can easily by-pass a host of relevant moral concerns and bring about parenthood as a mere technologized achievement. On the other hand, authentic parenthood, that is, full motherhood or fatherhood, is a personal realization that arises from a highly moral context of love, marriage, and conjugal intimacy. A truly progressive civilization must regard mother- and fatherhood as personal and moral realizations, and not as mere technological achievements.

Separating procreation from loving sexual intercourse depreciate lovemaking, but it also weakens parenthood and the bond that love forms between parent and child. This point may be expressed in a variety of ways, from the shock expressed by one reporter who exclaimed: "People are conceiving not in clinches, but in clinics!" to sociologist George Gilder's more reflective assessment of the matter: "By circumventing the act of love, *in vitro* conception takes another step toward dislodging sexual intercourse from its pinnacle as both the paramount act of love and the only act of procreation. It thus promotes the trend toward regarding sex as just another means of pleasure, and weakens the male connection to the psychologically potent realm of procreation." [10]

3) Embryo Transfer

Embryo transfer goes a step beyond what is logically implied by *in vitro* fertilization. With embryo transfer, an embryo (whether or not formed through IVF) that has already implanted in the uterus is removed and transferred to the uterus of another woman. This technique is made available, fundamentally, for women who cannot conceive a child but are able to carry a child to term. A volunteer conceives the child (usually through artificial insemination) and then surrenders that child to the woman who will complete the period of gestation.

This technique effects the separation of pregnancy from motherhood and therefore assigns "motherhood" to various women on a limited basis. One woman supplies the egg, another the womb, yet a third might raise the child and supply the love and guidance. A child, therefore, may have three mothers: a genetic mother, a gestational mother, and an adoptive mother. "We need to do a total rethinking of the notion of parenthood," writes Lori Andrews, a research attorney for the American Bar Foundation, and author of *New Conceptions*, a guide to the new reproductive techniques. "We don't even have a word," she adds, "that describes the relationship between a woman donating an embryo and a woman who is carrying the child."[11]

Two parents who are related to each other by virtue of a common relationship to a child are usually called husband and wife, and their relationship with each other is a spousal one. But the genetic mother is not the spouse of the gestational mother. These women may not even know each other. In our fragmented world of technologized parenthood, they may be regarded as partial parents, each contributing a part of what a traditional mother contributed by herself as a whole.

When the Harbor-U.C.L.A. Medical Center, the southern campus of the medical school of the University of California at Los Angeles, wanted to attract volunteers for its embryo-transplant project, it placed the following ad in several community and college newspapers covering the South Bay area of Los Angeles:

> HELP AN INFERTILE WOMAN HAVE A BABY.
> Fertile women, age 20-35 willing to donate an
> egg. Similar to artificial insemination. No surgery
> required. Reasonable compensation.

Nearly 400 women responded to the ad, one of whom later

became the genetic mother of the first child to come into the world as a result of the embryo transfer procedure. The staff at the Medical Center referred to their program as the Embryo-Transfer Project.

The ad and the project are willfully deceptive. A volunteer was not asked merely to donate an egg or ovum. She was asked to become pregnant in a manner that implied adultery, to undergo an early-stage abortion, and give her child up for adoption. In addition, she was asked to assume two rather serious risks in the event the lavage technique designed to remove her embryo failed. Either the child would be destroyed, or her pregnancy would persist. In the event the pregnancy persisted, she would be faced with either choosing a conventional abortion or carrying an unwanted pregnancy to term. She was also asked, by calling the child she conceived an "egg," to deny her own motherhood in this instance. It was convenient, from a merchandising point of view, for the Ovum Transfer Project to emphasize as much as possible the motherhood of their clients, who were to gestate the child, by denying the "partial" motherhood of the genetic mother.

By involving human reproduction with reproductive middlemen, and linking it more and more with principles of business and marketing, parenthood becomes increasingly arbitrary and may be assigned and re-assigned at will. Parenthood ceases to be an aspect of one's identity as a human being, and becomes a title that one is able to purchase for a price. When the ad asks a fertile woman to donate an egg, it is trading on those altruistic sentiments that are evoked in human beings when they are asked to donate blood or to donate to the heart fund. But donating blood and donating one's own child are radically different from a moral standpoint. It is inhuman as well as unjust to treat a child as a donatable commodity. It is also unjust to mislead a woman into thinking that her embryo is only an egg.

One gestational mother in the Ovum Transfer Project expressed elation that, as she put it, "someone else's egg has grown in my body." [12] She expressed a desire to thank the genetic mother, but the latter does not know she is the donor. In 1982, Doctors Alan Trounson and Carl Wood of Melbourne's Monash University pioneered a method of freezing the surplus ova that their IVF patients did not need. In cases where an egg is frozen before it is thawed and fertilized, a woman may never know whether she is a mother. She is the female counterpart of the anonymous sperm donor. To her, her own motherhood is made hypothetical.

Closely associated with embryo transfer is a procedure known as embryo adoption. The technology is the same, but with embryo adoption donor semen is used instead of the semen of the recipient's husband. As the name suggests, with embryo adoption, a couple has no genetic link to the embryo it adopts. Therefore, the child of embryo adoption has four parents: one who supplied the sperm, one who provided the egg, one who furnished the womb, and the male who raised the child as its father. What rights and status each of these parents has remains for the courts to decide. For example, do the parents who provided an adopted embryo's egg and sperm have visitation rights after that child is born? No doubt highly complex questions concerning intestate succession and will construction will have to be settled by the courts.

4) Extracorporeal Gestation

Extracorporeal gestation refers to the process by which the prenatal child is allowed to develop to term completely outside the woman's body in an artificial womb. No such womb has been developed to this point which could incubate a human being from conception to birth, but research continues. Scientists have predicted its arrival by the year 2,000.[13] Bernard Nathanson contends that an artificial womb will be perfected much sooner. "A feasible artificial placenta is on the horizon," he writes, which he believes will lead to a reliable life-support system for the pregnancy outside its original host womb.[14] Nathanson also believes that such artificial uteri will be produced in sufficiently large quantities to solve the abortion controversy by providing incubation for all those unwanted fetuses who are deprived of a mother's womb.

Joseph Fletcher welcomes the artificial womb because it makes pregnancy more accessible to the scrutiny of watchful scientists:

> The womb is a dark and dangerous place, a hazardous environment. We should want our potential children to be where they can be watched and protected as much as possible.[15]

Isaac Asimov concurs, arguing that an embryo developing outside the body can be more readily monitored for birth defects and, eventually, for desirable gene patterns. But he also endorses extracorporeal gestation because it would help women gain an important measure of equality with men. If a woman could "extrude the fertilized ovum for development outside the body," he writes, "she would then be no more the victim of pregnancy than a man is."[16]

The Italian embryologist Daniele Petrucci claims to have developed an artificial uterus in which he kept a female human embryo alive for as long as 59 days. Progress is being made all over the world in developing an artificial womb, yet replacing the give-and-take equilibrium that exists between mother and child poses immense difficulties. Given such problems, the suggestion has been put forward to use nonhuman animals as surrogate mothers. Recently, cows have been suggested to serve as host "mothers." Emeritus professor of gynecology Ian Donald at Glasgow University states: "I can foresee the day when a human baby is born to a chimpanzee. That might happen within 20 years."[17] Edwards and Steptoe, who delivered the world's first IVF baby have proposed that human embryos be implanted in such animals as sheep, rabbits, and pigs in order to study their early development.[18]

Given the maternal significance that tradition has attached to the gestational period, the artificial womb would seem to be a candidate for the title "mother." Inevitably, journalists will be writing about artificial or mechanical mothers. And if a cow were ever used to gestate a human child, new meaning would be given to the appellation "cowboy."

Current research on the subject of prenatal development indicates that the fetus is very much aware of his surrounding environment. For example, a newborn infant is able to distinguish his mother's voice from that of another woman, presumably from having heard it while being in the womb. Boris Brott, conductor of Ontario's Hamilton Philarmonic Orchestra, tells of an extraordinary musical experience he had which very well may be connected with his pre-natal life in the womb. While rehearsing a new musical score, Brott had a strong feeling of *déja vu*. Though he had never seen or heard the piece before, somehow he already knew the cello part. Intrigued, he queried his mother, who is also a musician, and discovered that she had been rehearsing the same score while pregnant with him.[19]

Psychiatrist Tom Verny has reported in his book, *The Secret Life of the Unborn Child* (1981), that babies in the womb can experience a startling variety of sensations and emotions. To Verny, Boris Brott's story would not be at all surprising. But how deprived would a human fetus be if it developed in a metallic or bovine environment? One embryologist, Robert T. Francoeur, is most emphatic in his answer: artificial wombs, he says, would produce nothing but psychological monsters."[20]

George Gilder fears that extracorporeal gestation on a large scale could ultimately make the womb obsolete.[21] If this came about, he reasons, women would lose their sexual appeal and cease to inspire men's love. By relegating procreation to science, the woman would forfeit her roles as wife as well as mother, and all the mystery and majesty that is inseparable from these roles. For similar reasons, Norman Mailer, in *The Prisoner of Sex*, closed his critique of radical feminism (which he regarded as essentially technocratic) by appealing to women not to "quit the womb."[22]

Extracorporeal gestation separates motherhood from parenthood most graphically, creating the impression that motherhood is something external to a woman's parenthood. But so basic a function of motherhood as gestation cannot apportioned to a machine or a nonhuman animal without seriously violating the integrity of motherhood. From the eminently realistic viewpoint of a woman's incarnate identity, extracorporeal gestation does not represent liberation, but self-rejection.

Ethicist Paul Ramsey has criticized various modes of technological parenthood for both depersonalizing and debiologizing human procreation.[23] These criticisms are perhaps nowhere more applicable than to extracorporeal gestation. To go a step further, extracorporeal gestation makes a woman's motherhood peculiarly discontinuous with her off-spring to the point that she may inaugurate, abandon, and resume her motherly relationship with her child almost at will. She is initially a mother (genetically), but upon relegating the gestational phase of her motherhood to an artificial womb, she appears to discontinue her motherhood which she may later resume once the child is born.

Extracorporeal gestation makes parenthood the abiding relationship between mother and child and offers the woman opportunities for interrupting and resuming motherhood at her convenience. It also makes the profound biological tie with her child that established during pregnancy an optional matter.

5) Surrogate Motherhood:

A surrogate mother is a woman who agrees to be insemi-nated with the sperm of a man whose own wife is not capable of either conceiving or carrying a child to term. She also agrees to relinquish any rights to the child and, once it is born, to deliver it into the custody of the sperm donor and his wife. For their services, surrogate mothers have received financial compensation that usually ranges from $5,000 to $30,000. Hence they are sometimes called "mercenary mothers."

The designation "surrogate mother" is misleading because it denotes that she is a substitute mother and therefore not the real or original mother. The surrogate mother is indeed the mother of the child, both genetically and gestationally. She is called a "surrogate" merely for psychological and commer-cial reasons in order to help the infertile woman, for whom the child is carried, feel that it is she who is the original mother. Such artful playing with language is a good indication of how easy it is to reapportion motherhood for reasons of conve-nience. To refer to a surrogate mother as an adultress who rents her womb and gives up her child, though accurate in most cases, is certainly contrary to sound merchandising prin-ciples.

Legal experts are well aware of the fact that in the event a surrogate mother should change her mind and decide to keep her child, she would have that right. The strength of her position lies in the fact that she is the natural mother of the child, a point that is often obscured by misleading language.

A disproportionately high ration of women who offer to carry babies for childless couples have had abortions. Dr. Philip Parker, a Michigan psychiatrist, found that of 125 women who took part in his study on surrogate motherhood, 26% had abortions. Parker believes that many of these women want to have another baby and give it away as a way of compensating for the child they aborted.[24] On the other hand, applicants accepted for surrogate motherhood by Noel Kane, a Michigan lawyer who popularized surrogate motherhood in the United States, all agree to have abortions if tests show the child they are carrying is deformed or mentally retarded.[25] Kane is owner of the Infertility Center of New York, a profit-making agency which is involved in what one *Time* reporter describes as "the controversial business of matching surrogate mothers with infertile *parents*"[26] (emphasis added).

The association between surrogate motherhood and abortion also raises the question of whether a woman who is carrying a child for another woman can exercise her prerogative to abort the child if her own health is threatened, or even for personal reasons. Would a legal contract bind a surrogate mother to deliver the child she carries (apart from health considerations); whereas a marriage contract and a spousal relationship would be less binding? Should law regulate forms of technologized parenthood more rigorously than forms of natural mother- and fatherhood? Should a woman be less free to abort the child of another man who is paying her a large sum of money to deliver his child than she is to abort her husband's child? On the other hand, can a lawyer for surrogate mothers *require* them to abort when there are problems with the pregnancy; whereas a woman's own husband cannot exact such a requirement?

The problems and issues that surrogate motherhood generates seem to be endless. We observe an instance of the confusion in reading the following ad for surrogates that appeared in a California newspaper and drew 160 responses: "Childless couple with infertile wife wants female donor for artificial insemination." [27]

A person might very well be led to believe that the advertiser is looking for a woman who will donate her egg for use in artificial insemination. The advertising couple was careful to avoid any reference to the word "mother," preferring to call a woman who conceives a child and carries it to term a "female donor for artificial insemination."

In Oak Ridge, Tennessee, a woman who already had a 10-year old son, served as a surrogate for her married sister who lived in New England. She presented her sister with a six-pound five-ounce baby girl.[28] In this case the baby girl was separated from her half-brother to be raised by her aunt, while regarding her own mother as her aunt. This confusion of identities and relationships is not uncommon among surrogate mothers. *Time* magazine did a personal profile on one surrogate mother who said of the child she conceived, carried, and delivered: "I feel like a loving aunt to her." [29] Technologized parenthood invariably causes women and men to take a detached view of their own motherhood and fatherhood. It makes it more difficult for them ot act in accordance with who they are because they are confused about their own identities.

The desire to help an infertile couple to have a child is unassailable, even praiseworthy. But even the most laudable desires are not immune to the ill effects of sentimentality. The desire to help a couple to have a child does not justify adultery, kidnapping, or child-bartering. Sentimentality all too easily obscures reason, which must remain clear if we are to be assured that the means we choose are moral.

Robert Francouer reports in his book *Eve's New Rib* an illuminating as well as amusing example of how a sentimental desire to help infertile couples can displace reason. At a convention of Catholic science teachers, a nun suggested that we might "update the charitable work of some religious communities and perhaps even establish a new order, a type of 'Sisters of Charity (or Mercy)' for the Substitute Mother." [30] This enthusiastic and altruistic nun was proposing, in the name of Christian charity, that a religious order would come into being consisting of surrogate Sisters who would bear the children of infertile couples!

The most celebrated case involving surrogate motherhood is one that offers a more powerful argument against its practice than any philosophical argument could. Surrogate mother

Judy Stiver of Lansing, Michigan, gave birth to a child in January 1983 with strep infection and microcephaly, a disorder indicating possible mental retardation. Alexander Malahoff, the man who had contracted for the child, decided he did not want it and told the hospital to withhold treatment. Mrs. Stiver stated that she had not established a "maternal bond" with the child since she had not held him. According to Michigan legislator Richard Fitzpatrick, "For weeks the baby was tossed back and forth like a football — with no one having responsibility."

Then, as a macabre touch that Boston University health-professor George Annes said makes the soap operas appear pallid, Malahoff and Mr. Stiver had blood tests to establish the child's paternity and went on the "Phil Donahue Show" to await the results. During the show Donahue announced that Malahoff was not the father. The Stivers had intercourse shortly prior to the artificial insemination procedure; the child was genetically theirs.

Malahoff reacted by suing the Stivers for not producing the child he ordered and is attempting to recover the $30,000 he paid out in related expenses. The Stivers sued the doctor, lawyer, and psychiatrist of the surrogate program for not advising them about the timing of sex. Incredibly, the Stivers, who agreed to appear on the Donahue show, took Malahoff to court for violating their privacy by making the whole affair public. And finally, the Stivers claimed that their child's illness was caused by a virus transmitted by Malahoff's sperm.[31]

University of Texas law professor John Robertson states that current laws insufficiently protect what he terms "collaborative reproduction." His term is an interesting one because it implies neither motherhood, fatherhood, parenthood, marriage, or even procreation. It represents in two well chosen words the logical end result of technologized parenthood. "Collaborative reproduction" does not describe human procreation or mother- or fatherhood; it speaks of the tangled and impersonal world of our modern techno-bureaucracy.

Conclusion

When we consider the various modes of technologized parenthood collectively, we discover that no feature of biological parenthood is considered indispensable for either mother- or fatherhood. With artificial insemination by donor (AID), a husband becomes a father despite the absence of his sperm, while his wife consents to conceiving a child by a man to whom she is not married; with artificial insemination by the husband (AIH), a man becomes a father apart from the conjugal embrace. With IVF, husband and wife become parents independently of sexual intercourse. In embryo transfer, a woman is considered a mother even though she is not the genetic mother. In extracorporeal gestation, a woman is called a mother even though she does not gestate a child. The surrogate mother foresees nursing and rearing her child, and the mother to whom she delivers the child is neither the genetic nor gestational mother.

Collectively, these forms of technologized parenthood exclude virtually all those features that are naturally and traditionally associated with mother- and fatherhood: marriage, sexual intercourse, the genetic contributions of husband and wife, gestation, nursing, and child rearing. It should be amply apparent that technologized parenthood not only produces attenuated forms of mother- and fatherhood, but threatens their very meaning.

Combining different modes of technologized parenthood may make its threat to motherhood and fatherhood all the more salient. Lori Andrews speaks of "a busy career woman (who has) one of her eggs fertilized with her husband's sperm in a Petri dish and then implanted in another woman."[32] This same woman could arrange for her child to be reared by what some sociologists call "professional parents." And if this woman were single and had her egg fertilized by a donor's sperm, she would have avoided marriage, intercourse, conception, pregnancy, gestation, lactation, nursing, and child-rearing, and still have retained the name *mother.* But in such a case, is the word "mother" anything more than an expression of will? Is this woman really a mother? Should not more be demanded of a mother than the donation of an egg?

To make matters even more confusing, some biotechnical revolutionaries would like to see men have children. Joseph Fletcher speaks enthusiastically about the prospect of a uterus being implanted in a human male's body and gestation achieved as a result of IVF and embryo transfer.[33] Fletcher also envisions hypogonadism being used to stimulate milk from the male's rudimentary breasts. The British magazine *New Society* claims that the technology to enable men to bear children is currently available and may eventually be utilized by homosexuals, transexuals, or men whose wives are infertile.[34]

Paul Ramsey has good reason to argue, then, that "When the transmission of life has been debiologized, human parenthood as a created covenant of life is placed under massive assault and men and women will no longer be who they are."[35] By this, Ramsey means that human beings will not be able to live morally, that is, "be who they are," if they do not understand that they are embodied persons, inviolable and incarnate unities of spirit and flesh. Neither a man nor a woman can "debiologize" themselves without denying and rejecting who they are as incarnate beings. Our modern scientific world has misled us into believing that matter is always something to be controlled, that thought is superior to flesh, that God's will is ever subject to technology's veto.

The various forms of technologized parenthood help people to have children, but they do not help to become mothers and fathers in the full sense of these terms. Having a child does not make one a *father* or a *mother*; it only makes one a *parent*. Motherhood and fatherhood are fulfilling realizations of personal realities; they necessitate a continuity between incarnate being and moral act. In this regard, the notion of *fruitfulness* is more inclusive than that of *fertility*.

Husband and wife are fruitful through a loving intercourse in which they affirm each other's distinctive personal reality as men and women in a way that creatively directs them toward the realization of their mother- and fatherhood. Fruitfulness, in contrast with fertility, is more than a mere exchange of gametes. One writer expresses this rich and elusive concept of fruitfulness between husband and wife in the following way:

> I not only affirm the unity of her person and nature as feminine but her integrity as an incarnate spirituality and its dynamism, that is, her possible maternity through which I, in turn, find my paternity as a self.[36]

A boy becomes a man, a man becomes a husband, a husband becomes a father. Similarly, we speak of the development of the girl who becomes a woman, a wife and a mother. These developments are by no means automatic; they require maturing processes, great personal effort, and the cooperation of other people and of culture in general. Technology, however, always plans to make things happen automatically. Its intervention in the area of human procreation clashes with the slow and arduous processes that prepare the emergence of mother- and fatherhood. Nature always takes time. Technology is impatient. Nature is evolutionary. Technology wants to repeat the past. The clash, therefore, is between a rational plan and a natural process, between impersonal expediency and personal expression.

We do not help people to grow and fulfill their destinies by encouraging them to employ forms of technological parenthood which create the impression that there is no essential difference between fertility and fruitfulness, parenthood and mother- and fatherhood.

Technologized parenthood feeds on a philosophy of rational dualism that separates matter from morals and structure from activity. One does not behave as a mother or father simply because one is a parent in some legal or material way. It is not a legal document or biological claim that makes one an authentic mother or father. Rather, the basis is in one's incarnate personhood and the willingness to embrace the moral responsibilities that mother- and fatherhood entail. There should be a continuity between matter and morals, form and destiny. Mother- and fatherhood should flow from their source in personhood as nature flows from the hand of the Creator.

When Gerard Manley Hopkins wrote, "He fathers-forth whose beauty is past change," [37] he was drawing our attention to the fact that mother and father are verbs as well as nouns.

NOTES

1. Siegfried Giedion, *Mechanization Takes Command* (New York: W.W. Norton & Co., 1969), p. 718.

2. Wilbert, E. Moore (ed.), *Technology and Social Change* (Chicago: Quadrangle Books, 1972), p. 97.

3. Lori B. Andrews, "Embryo Technology," *Parents,* May 1981, pp. 64-5. See also Robert Francoeur, *Utopian Motherhood* (London: Allen & Unwin, 1971), pp. 1-4. Pancoast's unusual experiment is likely the first documented case of human artificial insemination. After Pancoast's death in 1889, a former student of his, Addison Davis Hard, brought this story to light with an article in Medical World in 1909. Dr. Hard urged the use of AID from respected and successful men who were free of the scourge of venereal disease with the intent of improving the human race and protecting women. His article met with mixed reaction: one doctor identified Pancoast's questionable use of AID as "ethereal copulation," whereas another doctor condemned it as raping a patient under anesthesia. AID is not always a prophylactic against transmission of venereal disease. As a result of using AID, some women have contracted A.I.D.S. Here the disparity between euphemism and fact is complete.

4. *Ibid.,* p. 65

5. *Ibid.*

6. 345 N.Y.S. 2d 430.

7. *People v. Sorenson* in Mark Coppenger, *Bioethics: A Casebook* (Englewood Cliffs, N.J.: Prentice-Hall, 1985) p. 5.

8. *Ibid.*

9. B.A. Santamaria, *Test Tube Babies?* (Melbourne: Australian Family Association, 1984).

10. George Gilder, "The Bioengineering Womb," *The American Spectator,* May 1986, p. 22.

11. Harris Brotman, "Human Embryo Transplants," *New York Times Magazine,* Jan. 8, 1984, p. 51. At a conference on "High-Tech Babymaking" in the Spring of '86 sponsored by the Women's Research Institute of Hartford College for Women, keynote speaker Gene Corea expressed her concern that women could become merely collections of body parts, divorced from their procreative power and with a more tenuous self. At the same press conference, Barbara Rothman expressed similar concerns about the process by which human reproduction is becoming "commodified." (*The Chronicle: Hartford College for Women,* Vol. 9, No. 1, Spring-Summer, 1986).

12. *Ibid.*, p. 46.

13. The prediction was made by the RAND Corporation/Douglas Aircraft studies. Cited in *Weekend Magazine,* Sept. 18, 1971.

14. Bernard Nathanson, *Aborting America* (Garden City: Doubleday, 1979, p. 282).

15. Joseph Fletcher, *The Ethics of Genetic Control* (Garden City, N.Y.: Doubleday, 1974), p. 103.

16. Isaac Asimov, "On Designing a Woman," *Viva,* November 1973, p. 8.

17. St. Louis *Post-Dispatch,* Sept. 9, 1984.

18. Kansas City *Star,* Dec. 20, 1984.

19. Pablo Fenjves, "When Does Life Begin?" *Woman's World,* Oct. 22, 1985.

20. "Man Into Superman: The Promise and the Peril of New Genetics," *Time,* April 19, 1971, p. 49.

21. Gilder, p. 23.

22. Norman Mailer, *The Prisoner of Sex* (New York: New American Library, 1971), p. 168.

23. Paul Ramsey, *Fabricated Man* (New Haven: Yale University Press, 1970), pp. 89 and 135.

24. "Abortions frequent among candidiates," Toronto *Globe and Mail,* Sept. 6, 1982.

25. *Ibid.*

26. Claudia Wallis, "A Surrogate's Story," *Time,* Sept. 10, 1984, p. 51.

27. Elaine Markoutsas, "Women Who Have Babies for Other Women," *Good Housekeeping,* April 1981, p. 96.

28. *Ibid.*

29. Wallis, p. 51. See also *The Buffalo News,* Nov. 8, 1985 where Mrs. King, who carried a child for her sister Carole Jalbert, said: "To this day, I feel like an aunt. I was just baby-sitting." See also *The Buffalo News,* June 26, 1986, "Woman Presents Sister with Gift of Triplets," concerning what may be the world's first set of "surrogate triplets," presented as a "gift" to an infertile sister.

30. Robert Francoeur, *Eve's New Rib* (New York: Harcourt Brace & Jovanovich, 1972), p. 20. Fr. Owen Garrigan, author of *Man's Intervention in Nature,* asks whether a priest would violate his vow of celibacy if he donated semen to a sperm bank.

31. *The Malahoff v. Stiver* lawsuit (No. 83-4734), was heard in federal district court in Detroit. Lori Andrews recounts the affair in the *American Bar Association Journal.* See also *Time,* Sept. 10, 1984, p. 53 and the Chicago (AP) wire service story in the Kitchener-Waterloo *Record,* Feb. 3, 1983, A10.

32. Lori B. Andrews, p. 67.

33. Fletcher, p. 45.
34. London (AP), Kitchener-Waterloo *Record,* May 9, 1981, front page headline.
35. Ramsey, p. 135.
36. Terence P. Brinkman, S.T.D., "John Paul II's Theology of the Human Person and Technological Parenting," *Technological Powers and the Person,* ed. Rev. A. Moraczewski, O.P., *et al* (St. Louis: The Pope John Center, 1983), p.377.
37. G.M. Hopkins, "Pied Beauty," *Gerard Manley Hopkins* (London: Unwin, 1953), p. 31.

II. THE ETHICS OF SUICIDE
By Ralph McInerny

I am a philosopher. My subject is suicide.

You may think this an odd coincidence. Then again you may not. After all, Dr. Johnson had a friend who said he had been thinking of going into philosophy but somehow cheerfulness kept breaking through. Moreover, the Stoics developed a lugubrious rationale for bringing one's life to an end. More recently, the French philosopher Albert Camus declared that the first philosophical question was: Should I commit suicide? His reasoning was that any other question presupposes a negative answer to that one.

On the other hand, Socrates in his death cell, waiting for his ship to come in — the arrival of a ceremonial boat was to signal that his end had come — was urged by his friends to cheat the executioner but he spurned the idea with the observation that he belonged to the gods, not to himself, and he ought not destroy their property.

My subject is suicide because, as the presumably clear-headed choice of death, it is the complete antithesis of respect for life.

I address the topic as a Catholic philosopher, more specifically a Thomist, that is one who derives his main intellectual inspiration from an overweight medieval friar who died at 49 leaving a veritable library of writings which continue to have that odd timeliness we associate with genius.

Living in the second and third quarters of the 13th century and involved for much of his professional life in the tumult of the University of Paris, Thomas, unlike some of his fellow professors welcomed the incoming flood of pagan and Islamic learning but unlike others was a critical recipient of that enormous wealth of knowledge. He rejected both the view that there is a radical conceptual conflict between natural learning and religious belief such that philosophy must be regarded as a threat AND the insouciant view that, while there is this radical conflict, it doesn't matter. One can simply wear different hats on different occasions. Thomas held that truth cannot conflict with truth, that not all conflicts are real ones, that where conflict is real a supposed truth cannot be such, but that in any case there is no simple apriori test. One has to take a careful look and see.

It is not too much to say that if Thomas's view had not prevailed, medieval Europe would have become like the Iran of the Ayatollah and you and I would not be meeting here under the auspices of an institution with significant links to the medieval university. Because Thomas's view prevailed, the Church in speaking on ethical matters almost invariably appeals to moral commonplaces as well as to such guidelines as Scripture and tradition. The latter may motivate the believer, but the former provide a basis of action common to believers and nonbelievers. Thus contraception and abortion are not said to be wrong for Catholics alone but for anyone and they can be seen to be such by reflecting on what is being done and how. The moral commonplace to which such judgments appeal as to premises have come to be known as Natural Law Precepts.

Suicide may be thought of as the isolated act of a troubled individual, an act which, as a human act, has implicit in it a supposedly justifying reason. It may be, of course, that what looks like a human act is not, that the person is so troubled or terrified or tortured we would hesitate to regard what he does as responsible, a deed for which he can answer. So regarded, suicide poses quite special problems, problems which do not so much affect what we mean by suicide as its applicability to this case or that.

But it is not thus that I shall address the subject. We live in a time when there are advocates of the right to suicide, when there is, O Shades of Socrates, a Hemlock Society — the cultural and historical opacity of those who would this evoke the memory of that Athenian sage as warrant for a deed he spurned is of itself a sign of the times — when it is maintained that the medical profession has no right to refuse the patient who requests a fatal dose of morphine, a request which will have been made perhaps years earlier at a time of presumed lucidity of mind. It is this quite special scenario in which the patient claims a right to die and the doctor asserted to have a duty to kill that interests me in the following remarks.

What I have to say could be billed as on life, medicine and natural law, that is, on just about everything. By life is meant human life, medicine is the art devised to heal the sick and handle threats to the physical well being of humans, and natural law consists of those moral commonplaces already alluded to. I shall try to say something intelligible involving all three of these. If I fail I will, of course, slash my wrists, fall on my sword and otherwise make a nuisance of myself.

Perhaps I need not warn you that it is a function of the philosopher to state the obvious, to begin with simple matters and perhaps to end with them as well. For some of us this is as much necessity as choice, but we try to get credit for it anyway.

1. The Human Race Lives by Art and Reasoning

Aristotle came to occupy pride of place in late medieval philosophy as the result of the controversies alluded to earlier. For Thomas, and then for many, Aristotle was simply The Philosopher. Quite apart from his overwhelming teaching tasks, Thomas on his own time commented line by line on almost all the works of Aristotle, a moonlighting effort accomplished in five years during the most frenetic period of his career. This eagerly receptive attitude toward philosophy was decisive for Thomas's theology. He is always on the *qui vive* for the truths which unite believer and nonbeliever even as he reflects on the mysteries of his Christian faith. Thus while he does not expect the nonbeliever to hold as true the Trinity, the Incarnation, etc., the example of Aristotle grounds his conviction that the nonbeliever can from the things of this world, the things that are made, come to some knowledge of the invisible signs of God. The pagan Aristotle had done it. Thus one can speak of God to nonbelievers and fashion arguments which presuppose His existence without thereby retreating into theology proper, without the necessity of presupposing Revelation and divine faith.

(*Aside.* The believer's thought experiments in which he looks at the world as it appears to one without faith should not be seen as ingratitude on his part, as if he somehow envied those without the gift of faith. His purpose is to find a point of contact with the nonbeliever. But his efforts will have the added value of showing him the reasonableness of belief, the defensibility of accepting as true what we cannot in this life *see* to be true. It is of course the height of impiety, even blasphemy, to suggest that the faith is a vacation from reason, a carefree acceptance of nonsense.)

Thomas does not expect the nonbeliever to be guided by the demands of Charity, but the principles of justice are common to all and do not depend on the acceptance of any revelation.

In the matters of suicide and euthanasia, Thomas's specifically Christian views are easily stated. Both these acts are violations of Charity which enjoins one to love his neighbor as himself. Self-love being the measure of love for others, and killing oneself not being interpretable as doing oneself good, suicide manifestly violates charity. So too killing another person in the circumstances envisaged by living wills violates charity.

Binding, a German doctor who advocated the doing away with what he termed useless life, somewhat unctuously asserted that his views were in keeping with good religion. It can be safely said that he held a theological position opposed to that of Thomas Aquinas. In discussions of these matters one often hears that "my God does not enjoy seeing people in pain and would approve of ending it." As a mere philosopher, I will not argue the point on specifically Christian premises. That is not my role in the Church and, even if it were, discussing from a formally theological viewpoint would limit the relevance and interest of the discussion to Christians. If Thomas and the Church had only theological arguments — perhaps they would now be called arguments from Christian ethics — these could not be relevant as such to a pluralistic society like our own. When Thomas does moral philosophy, as opposed to moral theology, he sounds a good deal like Aristotle. Not least because he engages in this humble enterprise in the course of commenting on moral works of Aristotle, the *Nicomachean Ethics* and the *Politics.* But whether in his philosophical or theological writings, the echo of Aristotle is everywhere.

The Aristotle of the opening of the *Metaphysics,* first of all. There, from the initially improbable assertion that all men by nature desire to know, Aristotle develops a magnificent panorama of human life in which our species is seen as the epitomization of the cosmos, man a microcosm in which inorganic, vegetative and animal characteristics are found together with that something more that distinguishes us from all the rest. Mind. Awareness. "The human race lives moreover by art and reasoning."

In this context art is first used to convey any generalization from experience. "Now art arises when from many notions gained by experience one universal judgment about a class of objects is produced." It is wholly typical of Aristotle that he should illustrate what he means by a medical example. (His father was a physician but died when Aristotle was quite young, so watching his father does not seem to be the origin of Aristotle's predilection for medicine. Some maintain that Aristotle himself was a physician.) It is one thing to know that such and such a procedure helped Socrates and Callias and others; it is quite another to know why the procedure will help anyone in such and such conditions. "This is a matter of art." *Techne.* Here the discussion branches off. In practical matters, experience does not seem inferior to art. Far from it. One who has theory without experience will usually fail to cure. Nonetheless, experience informed by theory is best. In theoretical matters, the universal judgment is unequivocally desirable.

This use of the word *techne* to speak of science is unusual in Aristotle. What is not is the invocation of art as a point of reference. When he speaks of the constitution of physical objects, he will talk of the making of things by a human agent. When he speaks of human action, he will exemplify it by the activities of artisans and then ask if there is some good beyond the specific good of the artisan's activity. The point of shoe-making is to make good shoes, but is engaging in this activity successfully always a good thing to do? The objective of the medical art seems almost to fuse the moral appraisal and that intrinsic to the practice of medicine. A discussion of the pure technique of resoling loafers can be carried on without a sense that weighty ethical issues are huddling in the wings. But medical procedures bearing as they do on a human person can seem all but indistinguishable from moral action *tout court.* A purely technical discussion of them would seem contrived. Or menacing.

2. The Medical Art

An art consists in the know-how to produce something or other. It is a virtue of the practical intellect, that is, the acquired skill to do well what we must do in any case. Practical wisdom or prudence is another virtue of practical mind and art and prudence are said to differ in this way. Art seeks to perfect its product, that is, make it a good one; prudence seeks to perfect the agent as such, that is, make him good.

Another contrast. Art and nature. The tree under which we seek shelter from the rain differs from an umbrella. The first is produced by nature, the second by art. But the artifact has the natural as its base. In its first and clear instances, art is a transformation of nature. The tree is cut into lumber, the lumber is used to make a house. Synthetic materials are very complicated artifacts, not creations *ex nihilo.* The artifact incorporates the end or purpose of the artisan which limits the natural material that can become a component. Leather is good for shoes, bark is not, ice less so, water is useless. The reverse of this is to notice that the artisan has to know the way things are, take it into account, in order to perform his task well. Art is constrained by nature.

Art is also said to imitate nature. The example is medical. In binding up the wound, the doctor is aiding nature's healing process, perhaps in such a way that if he did not help, nature would not be able to act. Surely only a philosopher would be willing to say in public that a doctor must know something of the human body in order to cure it. It's not that anyone would deny it; it's that no one else thinks it needs saying. It is the physical well being of the body the physician seeks to restore, preserve, enhance. Another truism. He does not *decide* what the well-being or health of the body is. He starts from that as a given. More than any other artist, the physician must be alert to the nature with which he deals; more than any other artist, the physician is engaged in an activity which will be morally appraised. It will be well to say what such a moral appraisal is, but first an odd fact about the human being.

If nature and art are contrasted it is nonetheless true that man is naturally an artisan. It is of the essence of being human that we rearrange nature for our purposes. The arts of fishing and farming and hunting are necessary for survival, as is the art of shelter-building. Homo faber. It is the sign of man's preeminence in nature that he enters the world unshod, unarmed, provided with no natural home; he is more possibility than actuality, inchoate, but he has been given something better, two things, actually, the prehensile hand and a mind. With these he can fend for himself, and must. Nature is there for him to work on.

It is easy to see medicine emerging in that setting and easy to see how it will be appraised. Health and well-being, no more than food and drink and shelter, no more than reproducing and living in the community, are not things men decide are good. When we reflect on our doings, we see that we have always already been pursuing these things as unquestioned goods. Since they can be pursued well or badly — people overeat, covet the spouses of others, build on sand, and so forth — we must put our minds to doing them well. It is not up to us to want these goods, but the way to them is up to us. And figuring out which of the possible ways are good and which are wrong. What are the criteria for good and bad action?

I have come this circuitous and reminding way so that I can point out that those who plead for suicide and euthanasia see themselves in the light of these presuppositions of human action and its moral appraisal. The proponent thinks he has to justify the allowing of suicide by appeal to some premiss or principle. What is it? He is at pains to justify euthanasia by appealing to a premiss or principle. What is it? In both cases, it seems to me to be this: What the suicide *wants*. What the putative beneficiary of euthanasia *wants*. And what is the object of their wanting? In the case of euthanasia, we hear of wanting to live or not wanting to live. Those seem to be basic. There seems no way in which we can ask whether wanting to live is a good thing or not wanting to live a bad thing. There seems no way to suggest that not wanting to live may be not so much bad, as impossible. Just as wanting to live is not so much an option as a constituent of what we are.

3. The Natural Law View

Natural Law is not put forward as one theory among many possible ones. If Natural Law is true then in some sense everyone already holds it, whether or not by that name. If not, a person would have to be persuaded to accept natural law on some basis or other. That it accords with her most basic views of good, for example. But whatever is appealed to would have to be itself a constituent of natural law. That is, anything I would appeal to, on the assumption you already hold it, that anyone would hold it, in order to get you to accept natural law, would be itself natural law, that is, a fundamental basis for choice. Not even all proponents of Natural Law seem adequately frank about this: natural law precepts are non-gainsayable.

The analogy is with the principle of contradiction. To deny it is to accept it. "A thing cannot be and not be at the same time and respect." Call that P. Imagine someone crying, Not-P. In order for his denial to make sense what he denies must be presupposed. Now no one really likes this kind of argument after the age of 21 or so. But it is unanswerable. It doesn't prove so much as it shows no proof is needed.

Is the desirability of life nongainsayable in that way?

Albert Camus began a famous book by saying that the first philosophical question is: Should I or should I not commit suicide? But he saw that to discuss it is already to answer it in the negative. Indeed, knowing the true answer seems more important than snuffing oneself. Is that sufficient?

What Camus enables us to see is the obvious, namely, that human action is as such conscious action, it is doing something with an eye to something or other. And at the bottom of it all are inclinations, desires, we cannot not have. Any formulation of the human good must begin with the objects of such inclinations. Those objects will be constituents of the human moral good insofar as they are implicitly or explicitly known. We can be said to have known them implicitly when, hearing them explicitly stated, we say, of course. As when

Camus makes explicit what is presupposed in asking questions. Namely, that the truth is not something we can decide is the good of thinking. We recognize that it is and we knew it all along.

Life is that kind of a good. Indeed, it is the most basic good of that kind. That is why it is difficult even to follow discussions which ask whether living is or is not desirable. Living in pain is not desirable, but is it clear that to live and to live in pain are through and through identical? When they are, the agent — who is presumably also a patient — would seem to be incapable of performing any human action. What if the conditions that make suicide morally acceptable also render moral action and thus the doing of it impossible? Or would the fear that such conditions might obtain justify a preventive strike against them?

You can see that there is a fairly quick way in which the morality of suicide can be handled. One could argue that the decision to commit suicide does not qualify as a moral choice at all, that it is intrinsically incoherent.

Something or other can be desired, pursued or chosen only insofar as it is good for me, and that means, fulfilling of me or a constituent of what if fulfilling of me. Anything that could qualify as good in that sense presupposes my existence once it is attained. Thus, my ceasing to be cannot be chosen as a good. Ceasing to be cannot be my good.

The fact that people choose it or seem to choose it cannot affect that. People overeat but that does not mean that obesity is good for us. It does mean that overeaters think that food in limitless quantities is good, and they can think this because food is good and it is a constituent of the human good. The glutton pursues a good in a disordered way, that is, without reference to its part in the total good. One might argue that what the suicide wants is a pain-free existence, an existence minus whatever has brought him to such despair and anxiety. It is not non-existence as such he wants, but not existing in such and such a way. On this construal, suicide would involve a tacit belief in life beyond death.

A believer who hears the proponent of euthanasia assert that it is barbaric to imagine that God should want us to suffer pain, might be led to ask him what from a Theistic view the point of pain might be. In any case, it might have led him to the recognition that made the pagan Socrates reject the advice that he cheat the executioner and commit suicide. Socrates replied that he did not own himself. He was God's. He had great but limited power over what he might permissibly do. He saw life as a gift. The arch suggestion that the suicide is simply returning the gift can scarcely be a serious acceptance of what is going on. Pagans as well as believers have seen the ultimate point of life as beyond the present one. Returning the gift on this view does not restore one to the *status quo ante*, that is, nothingness, but is rather rushing to a judgment that might prove more exacting than the pain fled.

But no one here will imagine that the friend of suicide intends those religious asides to be taken seriously.

4. Some Objections

There are difficulties to the outlook I am representing which arise from within it and it may be well to look at some of them.

Medicine is an art and one which especially is taken to manifest the claim that art imitates nature. The physician, knowledgeable in the functions and aims of the human body, bends his best efforts to seeing that the organism is sound, that malfunctions are remedied, and so on, being guided by what nature intends.

But death is natural. No organism is destined to go on forever. Mortality isn't a disease, but a condition of existence of the human organism. There comes a season in life when the body wears out, develops malfunctions, is invaded by malignancies. Teeth fall out, eyes weaken, hearing is less acute; the limbs stiffen up, aches and pains and then some terminal illness comes. Surely the point of the art of medicine is not to fly in the face of such facts and see death itself, mortality, as what must be cured. All cures are temporary. In certain conditions death is inevitable, not just logically, but with close predictability. How much longer do I have to live? About six feet.

Well, then, does it not fall to the physician to help nature achieve her ends? Nature is sloppy and prolonged and haphazard in bringing a life to its close. A point is reached where one will never play the violin again. Why not, in this Aristotelian-Thomistic context, agree with Binding and Hoche and say a fatal shot of morphine can crown the efforts of the health-delivery systems.

Respondeo dicendum quod. To act in order to bring about the death of another is almost a definition of injustice, of the unjust act. To cause harm to another is unjust; death is the greatest evil; deliberately to cause another's death is to be guilty of the greatest injustice.

The fact that death is natural does not make it less an evil for a particular organism. That the chicken is the natural prey of the fox does not make being eaten a good of the chicken.

Objection: death is the greatest evil because without it none of the other human good can be enjoyed. But we are imagining a situation where none of those other goods will ever be enjoyed again. In these conditions, death is no longer the greatest evil but, arguably, the only thing worth choosing.
Response: Undeniably a state is reached where the continued existence of the patient seems vegetal at best. This rules out suicide as a possible action. Is euthanasia equally ruled out?

Nowhere is it more clear than in their discussion of comatose and imbecilic patients that Binding and Hoche, the medical theorists of the Third Reich, were not concerned about the well-being and good of these patients. Such patients are not described as being in pain. The problem is another one. They are a drain on the economy. They cause us pain of various kinds.

Nowhere are the two discussions thinner than at this point. What lessons may be drawn from the presence of the halt and the lame and the retarded in our midst? What lessons may be drawn from caring for the terminally ill, for patients moving inexorably toward death? To treat such patients as worn out or defective machines betrays a materialism that may wear the disguise of compassion or even religion but is for all that a failure to grasp the unique character of the human person at any point in her existence. To regard a suffering human person as one would a horse with a broken leg is unfortunate. Such an outlook, as Aristotle said in another context, requires punishment not instruction.

Lest someone else bring it forward, let me say that Aristotle himself is an unsure guide on the matters that concern us here. You may remember the famous 16th Chapter of Book VII of the *Politics* and marvel at the irenic way in which I have linked Aristotle and Thomas.

> As to the exposure and rearing of infants, let there be a law that no *deformed* child shall live, but that on the ground of an *excess* in the number of children, if the established customs of the state forbid this (for in this state population has a limit), no child is to be exposed, but when couples have children in excess, let abortion be procured before sense and life have begun; what may or may not be lawfully done in these cases depends on the quesion of life and sensation.

Deformed children can be exposed; others may not be. But couples who threaten to have an excess of children, can abort. The permission of abortion relies on false biological assumptions as to when life begins but Thomas, who shared those assumptions, would never condone abortion. There is no mitigation of the statement about the exposure of deformed children. And of course Aristotle's discussion of slavery in the *Politics* astonishes and repels us. Thomas's commentary on the *Politics* is not complete, alas; it breaks off long before the passage on exposure and abortion. He did deal with the question of slaves, but that is another matter.

Not entirely. It has to do with the human being as a person. In the recent Magisterial documents bearing on medical-ethical matters and generally on moral matters, there is an emphasis on the presuppositions of the moral judgments made. Cardinal Ratzinger's reply to questions having to do with *in vitro* fertilization, surrogate parenthood, etc. prefaced his remarks with a reminder that his answers will make little sense to us if we have lost the sense of the human being as a person whose dignity stems from that.

Euthanasia, since it cannot coherently be justified as for the good of the one killed, is justified by appeal to some political aim assumed to be of unquestionable overriding importance. But at best this is a parody of a moral argument. Absent some such supposedly overriding good, arguments for euthanasia are simply incoherent.

That there are evils which cannot simply be removed in a morally acceptable manner, by removing the patient, say, tells us something about the human condition. It is Mother Teresa and her sisters who attend men dying of AIDS, exhibiting by what they do their conviction of their worth and dignity. In like manner, it seems to me, it is those who recognize the limits of human action who will continue the advance of medicine, not those who see euthanasia as a form of healing.

Envoi

What, then, from a purely philosophical view can we say of the ethics of suicide? An ethical justification of suicide must argue that it is for the good of the suicide. But suicide aims at the non-existence of the suicide and thus the removal of him for whom suicide is said to be a good. There is no coherent way in which one can argue that suicide is good for you.

The hero, by contrast, puts himself in harm's way for the common good. Greater love no man hath than that he lay down his life for his friends. But the hero, or Savior, is not the instrument of his own death. Rather, he accepts the risk of it for the good of others. We should not permit that muddying of the waters that would equate the suicide and the hero.

III. TOWARD AN INTEGRAL PRESENTATION OF "HUMANAE VITAE" and "FAMILIARIS CONSORTIO" IN THE SEMINARY CURRICULUM*
By David Q. Liptak

Humanae vitae, Pope Paul VI's monumental and magnificent Encyclical, unquestionably sets forth the Church's certain and enduring doctrine on reverence for human life from the moment of conception, and on the sanctity of human sexuality and procreation. It is a doctrine which must form and bind conscience.[1]

Consequently *Humanae vitae* must be taught, studied, and pondered in the seminary; no priest can be doctrinally in union with his bishop and the Roman Pontiff unless he is capable of, willing, and ready to teach and defend this doctrine in his preaching, in his catechesis, in his counsel within the sacramental forum of Penance and outside it, in his role as pastor or religious educator, and, indeed, in his daily witness as a priest whose office cannot be clearly separated from his person. Such capability, willingness, and readiness begin in seminary academics and formation.[2]

Philosophy is the first major area wherein such formation takes place. In the course on the philosophy of man, for example, the view of man as unique, precious and unrepeatable must be set forth and analyzed. A human being can never be relegated merely to an "it"; on the contrary, always and everywhere, every human being is, in Martin Buber's celebrated phrase (one pioneered by the Catholic existentialist Gabriel Marcel), a "Thou" — always and everywhere some*one* and not some*thing*[3].

Our *philosophia perennis* has a clear vision of man as "subject" not "object". As Shakespeare puts it in *Hamlet:* "What a piece of work is a man! How noble in reason! How infinite

---

*Reprinted with permission from *"Humanae Vitae,"* 20 Anni Dopo, Atti del II Congresso Internazionale di Teologia Morale, Roma, 9-12 novembre 1988. Edizioni Ares, Milano.

in faculty! in form and moving how express and admirable! in action, how like an angel! In apprehension, how like a god!"[4]

Such a vision of man underlies the doctrine of *Humanae vitae*. Thus it should be cast and focused early in the seminary philosophy curriculum.

This is of course an area in which His Holiness, Pope John Paul II, has been working since his early days as an ethician. Reaching back into the thought of Socrates, Plato and Aristotle, the Holy Father has given Christian humanism a new existential interpretation. As one of his former students, Father Andrew Woznicki, now at the University of San Francisco, explains in his recently published *The Dignity of Man as a Person:*

> Christian humanism as viewed by the then Karol Wojtyla and the present John Paul II is based on two sets of human values: a synthesis of existence and love, and a connection between truth and freedom. Based on these two sets of human values . . . (Karol Wojtyla) lays down a new foundation for Christian ethics. On the one hand, Christian ethics, based on Wojtyla's existential personalism, is fulfilling the requirements of "naturalistic" humanism, because it takes into account both the individual experience and personal freedom of man . . . In the words of John Paul II: "to speak of 'ethos' means to recall an experience that every man, not only the Christian, lives daily . . . This experience is always connected with that of his own freedom, that is, the fact that each one of us is truly and really the "cause of his/her own acts". On the other hand, an ethical system which stems from Wojtyla's existential personalism is grounded in one's own experience of *"divinum"* (the "divine"): "In the ethical experience, therefore, there is established a 'connection between truth and freedom', thanks to which the person becomes evermore himself, in obedience to the creative wisdom of God".

Mention of the Holy Father's academic contributions

prompts thoughts about the whole school of Lublin Personalism or Lublin Existentialism, an invaluable assist in reasoning as to the truth of *Humanae vitae*. Lublin Personalism or Existentialism, which constitutes the Polish philosophers' gift to their Church, was cradled in the 1950's when the best insights of existentialists like Gabriel Marcel, Martin Heidegger, Karl Jaspers and Martin Buber, were incorporated within the framework of the perennial realist philosophy of St. Thomas Aquinas as interpreted by the French thinkers Jacques Maritain and Etienne Gilson; then related, in various degrees, to valid aspects of the methodology of phenomenology, especially that employed by Max Scheler and Roman Ingarden. This new system, whose description in fifteen volumes by extraordinary thinkers is currently being translated into English under the direction of the Reverend Francis J. Lescoe of the Archdiocese of Hartford and the Rector of Holy Apostles Seminary in Cromwell, Connecticut, has drawn heavily from Marcel. As Father Lescoe explained in his address as outgoing President of the American Catholic Philosophical Association in Baltimore, in May 1986:

"Some (of these insights) include the famous I-Thou relationship (also found in Buber); the notion of intersubjectivity and disponibility, which denotes a loving relationship between two subjects who, in turn, make themselves mutually available to one another and thereby co-create a new entity, a "we" *(nous)*. Lublin Personalism also subscribes to Marcel's insistence that "being" is superior to "having", that a person is always superior to the product or work which he/she performs"[6].

It likewise belongs to philosophy, in the seminary studies, in metaphysics as well as in the philosophy of man, to demonstrate *that*, and *how*, Platonic dualism is inadequate to explain the body-soul relationship in man. Philosophy must help the seminarian understand that the human soul is not just a spiritual substance making use of a body. To be a human being is, it should be carefully explained, "to be spirit expressed and made active through the body" — as Romano Guardini once put it.[7]

To relate all this to each person's origins, St. Thomas held that the soul shares its being with the body. Etienne Gilson taught that the soul "receives the body in the communion of its own act of being . . . Were it not so, the whole being of man would not be a substantial unity . . ."[8].

The Lublin Personalists summarize this teaching thus: "The human soul, having an actual relation to matter, is expressed through the body organized for the soul"[9].

All of the above means that one cannot realistically say, for example, "This is my body; I can do with it as I please." A similar protestation is made by some pro-abortion women's groups: "It's my body; consequently I can have an abortion if I so decide".

Also important here is a philosophical examination of, and a rejection of, Cartesian dualism.

Another discussion requiring a place in the seminary philosophical curriculum is an analysis of the creature, man, as contradistinguished from the Creator, God. To be a creature is not to be a being who finally rules and measures; God alone rules and measures. To be a man is to be one who *is ruled* and *measured*. As metaphysician Raymond Dennehy of the University of San Francisco has written:

" . . . the elan of post-Christian Prometheanism warns us that man's ontological reach extends beyond his ontological grasp. It induces in man a *"forgetfulness of his creaturehood and intrinsic limitation".* Secular humanism's failure to see that creaturehood is not a condition that can be overcome blinds their path"[10].

In the course on the history of modern philosophy, the theory of phenomenology can also be of substantial help for the seminarian who must later grasp *Humanae vitae* and *Familiaris consortio.* Some of the expressions in *Humanae vitae* reflect the idiom of phenomenology; for example, those in Section 12, which speak about "the two *meanings* of the conjugal act: the *unitive* meaning and the *procreative* meaning"[11].

And note these phenomenological nuances in *Familiaris consortio,* which develops the concept of the *meaning* of conjugal union:

"When couples, by means of recourse to contraception, separate these two *meanings* that God the Creator has *inscribed* in the being of man and woman and in the dynamism of their sexual communion, they act as arbiters of the divine plan and they "manipulate" and degrade human sexuality and with it themselves and their married partner by altering *its value* of "total" self-giving"[12].

Pope John Paul goes on to explain that contraception opposes "the *innate language*" that *expresses* the total reciprocal self-giving of husband and wife". This *language* is then overlaid, "through contraception, by an objectively *contradictory language;* namely, that of not giving oneself totally to the other"[13].

Also on the philosophical level, the course in ethics, besides providing seminarians with the traditional analysis of the moral act, the principle of the twofold effect and that the end can never justify an evil means, the principle of totality, and the reasons as to why some actions are intrinsically wrong and are hence never ethically defensible options (in other words that evil in itself can never be viewed as good), should at least introduce seminarians to the various inadequate or erroneous ethical systems most often summoned today in medical-moral, bioethical and sexual issues in support of the morality of human acts. This should include Kantian ethics, utilitarianism, and so-called situation ethics. Without a background knowledge of these theories, the theology student later may not be equipped to respond to challenges to *Humanae vitae* raised in the world as it exists, a world deeply confused and tainted by situation ethics, utilitarianism and Kantian modes of ethical judgment.

Doubtless, the best way to approach the subject of ethics is by reference to Karol Wojtyla's epoch-making book, *The Acting Person.*

Most of all, in a sense, the seminarian still in the philosophy curriculum must be initiated into the concept of the natural moral law. In *Gaudium et spes* we are remined to assess the conjugal act by standards "based on the nature of the human person and his or her acts" in order to "preserve the full sense of mutual self-giving and human procreation in the context of true love"[14].

The Church, it must be carefully explained to seminarians while still in philosophy, speaks of her fundamental moral doctrine as a "natural and gospel law". As Father Ronald D. Lawler summarized it during the first International Congress on Moral Theology in Rome in April 1986:

"It is a law rooted in our own natures, and in principle open to our own understanding. But it is also a divine law; through the prophets and Christ God himself has taught us how we are to live in love. There is no conflict in teaching that moral precepts are both naturally knowable and divinely revealed: the Church has always believed that the gift of revelation extends, to meet the needs of our fallen condition, to matters open in principle to our natural insight. Moral teaching in the Church has always been handed down primarily as a divine gift; the Church does not teach morality as a professor of ethics, judging that the precepts it hands on deserve respect only if the philosophical arguments that it offers in their defense seem persuasive to the hearer. She teaches morality prophetically, speaking for Christ" [15].

Thus the natural law, the seminarian must know, can be known in two ways: by rational insight into the reasons supporting it, and by faith in the word of God, whose moral revelation "supplies," it as it were, for our limitations in grasping what is really good[16].

Pope John Paul II, in his highly significant series of catecheses on *Humanae vitae* in 1984, made the point that — in his own words — "the norm of the encyclical concerns all men, insofar as it is a norm of the natural law and is based on conformity with human reason (when, it is understood, human reason is seeking truth)" [17].

In these catecheses during 1984, the Holy Father, Pope John Paul, amplified the teachings of Pope Paul VI in *Humanae vitae,* for example, in Section 4. Herein Paul VI refers to the key doctrines of *Humanae vitae* as "founded on the natural law", which, he adds, "the Church is competent to interpret" [18].

This is not to say, of course, that *Humanae vitae* is not part of the totality of Revelation. Paul VI, in the Encyclical, wrote of the natural law's in this case being "illuminated and enriched by divine Revelation" [19]. Moreover, Pope John Paul II, in his catecheses cited above, has stated:

"Even if the moral law, formulated in this way in *Humanae vitae,* is not found literally in Sacred Scripture, nonetheless, from the fact that it is contained in Tradition and — as Pope Paul VI writes — has been 'very often expounded by the

Magisterium' . . . to the faithful, it follows that this norm *is in accordance with the sum total of revealed doctrine contained in biblical sources"*[20].

It is a question here, the Holy Father went on, "not only of the sum total of the moral doctrine contained in Sacred Scripture, of its essential premises and general character of its contents, but of that fuller context to which we have previously dedicated numerous analyses when speaking about the 'theology of the body'."

"Precisely against the background of this full context it becomes evident that the above-mentioned moral norms belong not only to the natural moral law but also to the *moral order revealed by God;* also from this point of view it could not be different, but solely what is handed down by Tradition and the Magisterium, and, in our days, the Encyclical *Humanae vitae* as a modern document of this Magisterium"[21].

At this point of this paper, one is into theology, properly speaking, and here too an integral approach to *Humanae vitae* is essential. The doctrine of the Encyclical is covered from various aspects in several theological courses: human sexuality; marriage and family; bioethics; contemporary moral issues; moral virtues; the canon law of marriage; fundamental and moral theology, principles and precepts. It is also treated in the course on the Sacrament of Penance and in various pastoral courses.

It is in fundamental moral theology, clearly, that the full light of Revelation is cast upon objective morality; in this illumination it should become absolutely clear to the seminarian that so-called merely "ontic" or "pre-moral" acts are myths. Hence, the very assumptions of moral theories of proportionalism, which attempt to assess the morality of a proposed act exclusively by reference to the "good" or "bad" expected to proceed from it, and by "maximizing the good" while "minimizing the evil", are without validity. As Cardinal Joseph Ratzinger argued in the closing address to the American Bishops at Dallas on 10 February 1984:

"Since all moral questions have to do with persons, all moral theories should take the inseparability of the soul from the body into account. They should also take into account the fact that because it is only *people* who do actions describable as moral or immoral, all actions are automatically and immediately inseparable from the person who performs them. They cannot, therefore, be adequately described as merely ontic, since they always involve the person who performs them." [22].

In fundamental moral, too, divine truth illuminates the intrinsic immorality of directly taking innocent human life, as in direct abortion[23]. Here, also, in the basic moral courses, the principle of the twofold effect is studied, along with the norm that a good end cannot justify an evil means (example: direct abortion, sterilization, contraceptive intercourse). The principle of totality should also be restated here — a correct understanding of the "principle of totality" illustrated by Pope Pius XII in 1953 and 1956, for examples[24].

Likewise, in fundamental moral theology, Scriptural witnesses in behalf of reverence for human life from the moment of conception, and for the sanctity of human sexuality should be studied: texts such as Jeremiah 1:4-5; Psalm 139:13 sqq.; Luke 1:15; Luke 1:39 sqq.; as regards the holiness of human life from conception; and texts such as Matthew 5:27-28; 15:19, Mark 7:21-22; First Corinthians 6:19 and Chapter 7; John 2; Ephesians 5; also Genesis 2:4b-24; Genesis 1:2-1, 4a; and Genesis 1:31; as regards the holiness of human sexuality.

Fundamental moral theology is also a key area for developing the truth that the Church can, and in fact does, speak for Christ the Lord in matters of morality.

The validity and force of *Humanae vitae* rests not only on the fact that it treats of natural law refined by Divine Revelation[25]. More than this, the Encyclical constitutes "a pronouncement which the Pope was duty bound to make by virtue of the 'mandate entrusted to us by Christ' "[26]. Furthermore, the doctrine here was not set forth in passing, as it were; on the contrary, Paul VI intended to provide a decisive answer[27].

Surely there can be no questioning that the Church has irrevocably committed itself to the doctrine of *Humanae vitae*, which grounds the Apostolic Exhortation of Pope John Paul II, *Familaris consortio*, wherein the inner authencity and logic of Paul VI's Encyclical are developed in magnificent contemporary terms. Furthermore, the brilliantly structured and articulated "Instruction on Respect for Human Life in its Origin and on the Dignity of Procreation", issued by the

Congregation for the Doctrine of the Faith on 22 February 1987 and approved by Pope John Paul II, summons and marshals the enduring principles and norms of *Humanae vitae,* as well as those restated in *Familiaris consortio.*

Fundamental moral theology too is one locus for a discussion or dissent from Church moral doctrine: the validity, the limits, and the effect of such dissent. Cardinal Joseph Ratzinger spoke eloquently on this subject at a workshop for bishops in Dallas in 1984. Among other things he said:

". . . Important for us is the fact that private, personal dissent is to be distinguished from the dissent of a teacher, or the dissent of a theological specialist. Alienation from the community, even in the private, personal form, has grave implications for the spiritual life of the individual. On the other hand, because it is an individual, it is limited. Such is not the case for the teacher. A person who teaches in the name of the Church is taking what is basically a personal dissent and exaggerating its importance and its damage by propagating it. But the particular grave damage here is not simply that he teaches his dissent, but that he teaches it in the name of the Church. It is odd that people who have grave misgivings about the right of the Church to exist in any institutional form, seem to have no problem with the contradiction implicit in teaching in a Catholic school, which, after all, is an institution. Integrity seems to me to require that the person who dissents should not, precisely because he cannot, teach in the name of the Church, or even give that impression" [28].

In the classes on human sexuality, moral virtues, bioethics and/or contemporary moral issues, the personalistic nature of sexuality is rightly studied and brought into sharp focus with Revelation. Catholic doctrine on human sexuality and marriage can only be adequately understood if its *genuinely personalistic character* is grasped first. This is to say that human sexuality, in authentic Catholic thought, respects the person; furthermore, sexuality involves the person, *the total person,* and not simply his or her physical nature.

Conjugal union is in Catholic doctrine a mystery entailing a communion of persons. Conjugal union is not merely a bodily union, much less the joining of gametes. Conjugal communion, which has a language given it by God, is expressed through the body in accordance with God the Creator's will; John Paul II speaks of the "nuptial meaning" of the body.

Sexuality ultimately pertains to the *person*, therefore; masculinity and femininity go to the very soul of each man and woman. The human being must always be viewed in his totality, body and soul, soul and body. This is not to downgrade the body; the fact that Catholic theology considers the body so noble should not surprise anyone who reflects upon the meaning of the Incarnation. "Through the fact that the Word of God became flesh", declared Pope John Paul II in a General Audience, "the body entered theology — that is, the science, the subject of which is divinity, I would say — through the main door. The Incarnation — and the redemption that springs from it — became also the definitive source of the sacramentality of marriage . . ."[29].

Christians, therefore, are called to accept the theology of the body, including the nuptial meaning of the body. Again, though, a human being is a person, not merely a body; he or she is spirit expressed by body. Sexuality, thus, does not pertain to the body alone, but to the total person, body-spirit composite. Marriage is a union of persons united in life-giving and love-giving fidelity. When, therefore, it is taught that the life-giving (procreative) meaning of the conjugal act cannot morally be separated from the love-giving (unitive) meaning, the discussion proceeds from this personalistic basis, and not that of physicalism.

Finally, the doctrine of *Humanae vitae* also has its place in the courses in Mariology and eschatology, both of which remind us that, like Mary, we too are destined to be assumed to God, *body and soul*.

Teaching *Humanae vitae* in the seminary, the , is not simply a matter of a course or two. The doctrine in this profound and prophetic Encyclical rests upon a solid and dynamic vision of man, a vision which begins to emerge from reason — philosophy — and is refined and brought to completion in the divine light of Revelation. And even from the theological viewpoint, many courses, not just two or three, relate to *Humanae vitae*, courses which fit together as all truths meet in the overpowering luminescense of the Word of God, Light of the World.

The whole topic of reverence for human life from conception, as defended in *Humanae vitae,* is concretized in a news
photograph of Pope John Paul II taken at Auschwitz, in the
cell of the priest-martyr St. Maximilian Kolbe, during the Papal
visit of June 1979. The photograph, which a columnist in the
London Tablet described as surely one of the "pictures of the
century", showed the Holy Father telling his beads. According
to the caption, he was praying the fourth glorious mystery,
Maria Assumpta. As in Mary's case, God has drawn us to
himself too, in principle, all of us who keep faith. The
Assumption is a sign, even now, that each human being, from
conception, is unique, precious and unrepeatable, and meant
to rest in God, as Augustine so magnificently once expressed
it [30].

NOTES

1. Paul VI, *Humanae vitae*, trans. by NC News Service, St. Paul Editions, Boston 1968, Nos. 1-6; 19-31. No. 25 is especially significant. See also "Fidelity to the Truth in Love", Address of Pope John Paul II to Bishops of the United States Episcopal Conference at Quigley South Seminary, 5 October 1979, No. 6, in *The Message of Justice, Peace and Love*, St. Paul Editions, Boston 1979, pp. 183-84.

2. *Humanae vitae*, Nos. 28-30.

3. See Cardinal Joseph Ratzinger's comments in the press conference presenting the "Instruction on Respect for Human Life in its Origin and on the Dignity of Procreation" by the Congregation for the Doctrine of the Faith, 22 February 1987, in *L'Osservatore Romano*, English edition, 16 March 1987. See also *The Gift of Life* by Liptak D.Q. and Duffy L.T., M.D., Liturgical Publications, Milwaukee, WI 1988, p. 9. A summary analysis of Buber's thought appears in *Existentialism With or Without God* by Lescoe F.J., Alba House, Staten Island 1974, pp. 135ff.

4. Shakespeare, *Hamlet II*. ii. 298-302, in *The New Hudson Shakespeare*, ed. and revised by Charlton E., Ginn and Co., Boston 1909.

5. Woznicki A.W., *The Dignity of Man as a Person*, The Society of Christ, San Francisco, pp. 128-29. See also Woznicki A.W., *A Christian Humanism: Karol Wojtyla's Existential Personalism*, Mariel, New Britain, Ct. 1980, pp. 6-17; 30-62.

6. I cite from a copy of the typewritten text used by Father Lescoe. The address is published in *Existential Personalism, Proceedings of the American Catholic Philosophical Association*, Vol. LX, ed. by Daniel Dahlstrom, The American Catholic Philosophical Association, Washington 1986, p. 5.

7. Guardini R., *The Last Things*, University of Notre Dame Press, Notre Dame, Ind. 1965, p. 61.

8. Gilson E., *The Elements of Christian Philosophy*, Doubleday, New York 1960, pp. 222-29.

9. Krapiec M., *I-Man: An Outline of Philosophical Anthropology*, trans. by M. Lescoe, A. Woznicki, T. Sandok et at., Mariel, New Britain, Ct. 1983, p. 429.

10. Dennehy, R., *The Biological Revolution and the Myth of Prometheus*, in *Pope John Paul II Lecture Series in Bioethics*, Vol. II, ed. by Francis J. Lescoe and David Q. Liptak, Pope John Paul II Bioethics Center, Cromwell, Ct. 1986, p. 11. Italics added.

11. *Humanae vitae* No. 12. Italics added.

12. John Paul II, *Familiaris consortio*, Apostolic Exhortation, 22 November 1981, English trans. in *The Pope Speaks*, Vol. XXVII (no. 1, 1982), sec. 32, pp. 26-27. Italics added.

13. *Ibid.* Italics added.

14. *Gaudium et spes* in *The Documents of Vatican II*, ed. by Walter M. Abbott and Joseph Gallagher, Guild Press, New York 1966, sec. 51, p. 256.

15. Lawler, R.D., *The Magisterium and Catholic Moral Teaching*, in *Persona, Verità e Morale, Atti del Congresso Internazionale di Teologia Morale*, 7-12 April 1986, Citta Nuova Editrice, Roma 1987, pp. 222-23.

16. *Ibid.*, footnote. See also Denzinger-Schonmetzer 3005 and St. Thomas Aquinas, *Summa Theologiae*, I, q. 1, a. 1; 1-2, q. 91, a. 4.

17. John Paul II, *Catechesis of 18 July 1984, in L'Osservatore Romano*, 23 July 1984.

18. *Humanae vitae*, sec. 4., p. 5.

19. *Ibid.*

20. John Paul II, Catechesis of 18 July 1984.

21. *Ibid.*

22. Cardinal Ratzinger J., *Epilogue*, in *Moral Theology Today: Certitudes and Doubts*, Pope John Center, St. Louis 1984, p. 343.

23. *Humanae vitae*, No. 14.

24. *Ibid.*, No. 17, pp. 14-15. For Pope Pius XII, see AAS XLV (1953), pp. 674-75; AAS XLVIII (1956), pp. 461-62.

25. *Humanae vitae*, No. 4.

26. *Ibid.*, No. 6, p. 6.

27. *Ibid.*

28. Ratzinger, *Epilogue, cit.*, p. 340. See also *Ethics and Medics*, Pope John Center 9 (3), March 1984.

29. John Paul II, General Audience, 2 April 1980.

30. For this photograph see *w pielgrzymce do ojczystej ziemi, Jan Pawel II w Polsce 2 czerwca 1979. Nasza Rodzina paryz*, 1979, p. 168. The *London Tablet* commented on this photograph in the issue of 15 August, 1981, p. 787.

INDEX

ALSO AVAILABLE

$4.50 per volume

POPE JOHN PAUL II
LECTURE SERIES IN BIOETHICS

VOL. I

PERSPECTIVES IN BIOETHICS

I. CRITICAL REFLECTIONS ON CURRENT
BIOETHICAL THINKING
by Reverend Ronald D. Lawler, O.F.M. Cap., Ph.D.
Director of Thomistic Center
University of St. Thomas, Houston

II. "BEGOTTEN NOT MADE:" REFLECTIONS ON LABORATORY
PRODUCTION OF HUMAN LIFE
by William E. May, Ph.D.
Professor of Theology
The Catholic University of America
Introductions by: The Most Reverend John F. Whealon, D.D.,
S.S.L., S.T.L., Archbishop of Hartford
ISBN: 0-910119-00-3

VOL. II

BIOETHICAL ISSUES

I. THE BIOLOGICAL REVOLUTION AND THE MYTH
OF PROMETHEUS
By Raymond Dennehy, Ph.D.
Professor of Philosophy
University of San Francisco

II. A CHRISTIAN ETHICS OF LIMITING MEDICAL TREATMENT:
GUIDANCE FOR PATIENTS, PROXY DECISION MAKERS
AND COUNSELORS
by Germain Grisez, Ph.D.
Professor of Christian Ethics
Mount Saint Mary's College

ISBN: 0-910919-04-6

ANALECTA

VOL. I

SECOND CAREER VOCATIONS
by Cardinal Paul-Emile Leger et al.
trans. by Rev. Francis D. O'Hara, M.Ss.A., M.A. and
Rev. Francis J. Lescoe, Ph.D.

ISBN 0-910919-02-x

VOL. II

ACADEMIC COMPONENT OF PRIESTLY FORMATION

I. AVERAGE SUPERIORITY WILL DO
   by Professor Jude P. Dougherty
   Dean, School of Philosophy
   The Catholic University of America.

II. FAITHFUL AND CRITICAL REASON IN THEOLOGY
    by Reverend John Michael McDermott, S.J., S.T.D.
    Professor of Theology
    Gregorian University, Rome

ISBN 0910919-05-4

VOL. III

CATECHETICS

VATICAN I, ST. PIUS X AND THE UNIVERSAL CATECHISM
by Monsignor Eugene Kevane, Ph.D.
Visiting Professor of Catechetics, the Angelicum, Rome and
Holy Apostles College and Seminary.

ISBN 0910919-06-2

LIPTAK, David, Q., and Leo T. Duffy, M.D.
  The Gift of Life, Milwaukee, WI 33416-4633: The Liturgical Press,
    1988. $7.95   ISBN: 0-940169-06-1
  Back to Confession, Milwaukee, WI: Liturgical Publications, 1988.
    $6.95   ISBN: 0-940169-05-3
  The New Code: Laity and Deacons, Milwaukee, WI: Liturgical Pub-
    lications, 1985. $7.95   ISBN: 0-941850-19-6
  The New Code and the Sacraments, West Palm Beach, FL: Liturgical
    Publications, 1984. $7.95   ISBN: 0-941850-12-9

LESCOE, Francis J. and DUNCAN, Roger B., eds.
  M.A. Krapiec, I-Man: An Outline of Philosophical Anthropology. New
    Britain: Mariel Publications, 1985. $12.95
  Existentialism: With or Without God, New York: Alba House, 1974.
    $10.95